Project Manager: ZOBEIDA PÉREZ
Design & Art Layout: LISA GREENE MANE

Contents

After All (Love Theme From "Chances Are") .... CHER & PETER CETERA 3
Baby, Come To Me .... PATTI AUSTIN AND JAMES INGRAM 8
Beauty And The Beast .... CELINE DION & PEABO BRYSON 18
Burnin' The Roadhouse Down .... STEVE WARINER (DUET WITH GARTH BROOKS) 50
By The Time This Night Is Over .... KENNY G. FEATURING PEABO BRYSON 168
Count On Me .... WHITNEY HOUSTON & CECE WINANS 40
(I Wanna Take) Forever Tonight .... PETER CETERA & CRYSTAL BERNARD 24
House Of Love .... AMY GRANT AND VINCE GILL 64
How 'Bout Us .... GRAYSON HUGH & BETTY WRIGHT 60
I Finally Found Someone .... BARBRA STREISAND AND BRYAN ADAMS 74
I Will Always Love You .... DOLLY PARTON & VINCE GILL 13
If You See Him/If You See Her .... REBA AND BROOKS & DUNN 82
I'm Your Angel .... R. KELLY & CELINE DION 30
In Another's Eyes .... TRISHA YEARWOOD AND GARTH BROOKS 36
Maybe Not Tonight .... SAMMY KERSHAW & LORRIE MORGAN 98
Music Of My Heart .... GLORIA ESTEFAN AND *NSYNC 92
My Kind Of Woman/My Kind Of Man .... VINCE GILL WITH PATTY LOVELESS 120
Not Too Much To Ask .... MARY CHAPIN CARPENTER WITH JOE DIFFIE 143
On My Own .... PATTI LaBELLE & MICHAEL McDONALD 69
The Prayer .... CELINE DION AND ANDREA BOCELLI 130
Separate Lives (Theme From "White Nights") .... PHIL COLLINS & MARILYN MARTIN 104
Set The Night To Music .... ROBERTA FLACK WITH MAXIE PRIEST 162
Somewhere Out There .... LINDA RONSTADT AND JAMES INGRAM 55
Tell Him .... BARBRA STREISAND AND CELINE DION 114
Time To Say Goodbye (Con Te Partiró) .... ANDREA BOCELLI & SARAH BRIGHTMAN 87
Tonight I Celebrate My Love .... PEABO BRYSON WITH ROBERTA FLACK 146
Too Much, Too Little, Too Late .... JOHNNY MATHIS & DENIECE WILLIAMS 111
Up Where We Belong .... JOE COCKER AND JENNIFER WARNES 46
Valentine .... JIM BRICKMAN WITH MARTINA McBRIDE 124
When Something Is Wrong With My Baby .... LINDA RONSTADT & AARON NEVILLE 174
A Whole New World .... REGINA BELLE AND PEABO BRYSON 155
You Don't Have To Be A Star (To Be In My Show) .... MARILYN McCOO & BILLY DAVIS JR. 138
Your Love .... JIM BRICKMAN FEATURING MICHELLE WRIGHT 150

From the Tri-Star Pictures Film "CHANCES ARE"

AFTER ALL

(Love Theme from "Changes Are")

Words and Music by
DEAN PITCHFORD
and TOM SNOW

B
She:
E/G♯
A(9)
straight.
I still re-mem - ber when

C♯m7
F♯m
E/G♯
your kiss was so brand new.
Ev-ery mem-o-ry re-peats, ev-ery

A
E/G♯
Both:
A
B
A/B B
step I take re-treats. Ev-ery jour-ney al - ways brings me back to you. Af-ter
cresc.

Chorus:
E
C♯m
all the stops and starts, we keep com - in' back to these two hearts, two
f
F♯m
E/G♯
A
B
A
B
E
She:
an-gels who've been res-cued from the fall. Af- ter all that we've been through, it all comes
3
G♯m7
G♯/B♯
C♯m
Both:
A
He:
down to me and you. I guess it's meant to be, for

To Coda
1.
To next strain
Bsus
B
E
A/E
E
ev - er you and me,
af - ter all.
2. When love is tru - ly
dim.

2.
E(9)
Fine
Verse 2:
A(9)
He:
right,
(This time it's tru - ly right.)
rit.
mp

She:
E(9)
C♯m7
Both:
E/G♯
A
it lives from year to year.
It chang - es as it

D.S. 𝄋 al Coda
B
She:
E/G♯
A(9)
Both:
B
A/B B
goes, oh, and on the way it grows, but it nev- er dis- ap- pears. Af- ter
cresc.
Coda
E
Esus
(Bridge:)
Asus
Al - ways just be - yond my touch,
D.S. 𝄋 al Fine
G♯/B♯
C♯m
A
B
You know I need- ed you so much. Af- ter all, what else is liv- in' for? Af- ter

BABY, COME TO ME

Words and Music by
ROD TEMPERTON

F/G
G
Am7
D/A
Am7
D/A
ain't no sec-ond chance; you've got to hold on to ro-mance. Don't
F/G
G
F/G
G
Am7
let it slide. There's a
Bbmaj7
Am7
spe - cial kind of mag - ic in the air when you
Abmaj7
G11
F/G
G
find an - oth- er heart that needs to share. Ba - by,
cresc.

Chorus:
Cm7
Fm9
Ab/Bb
Fm
come (you.)
to me; —
let me put my arms a-round — you. This was
mf
Gm7
Ebmaj9
G7-9
meant to be, —
and I'm oh, so glad I found you. Need you
Cm7
Fm9
Ab/Bb
Fm
ev - 'ry day; —
got to have your love a-round — me. Ba - by,
Gm7
To Coda
1.
Dm7
G7-9
al - ways stay,
'cause I can't go back to liv - in' with-out

D.S. al Coda
2.3. etc.
D.S.S. al Chorus repeat and fade
Cm
Cm/B♭
B♭
Dm7
G7-9
you.
can't go back to liv - in' with-out
descresc.
Coda
Dm7
G7-9
Csus
can't go back to liv - in' with -out you.
C
A♭maj7
The night can get
Cm7
A♭/B♭
cold; there's a chill to ev -'ry eve - ning

2. Spendin' ev'ry dime to keep you
Talkin' on the line;
That's how it was, and
All those walks together
Out in any kind of weather,
Just because.
There's a brand new way of
Looking at your life, when you
Know that love is standing by your side.

To Chorus:

I WILL ALWAYS LOVE YOU

Chorus:
F Dm B♭ C F Dm
I will al - ways love you. I will
B♭ C F2 B♭m7/E♭ E♭7
always love you.
Dolly:
Bit - ter -
Verse 2:
A♭ A♭sus A♭ E♭/G Fm A♭/E♭
sweet mem-o - ries, that is all I am tak - ing with
D♭ E♭ E♭7 A♭ E♭/G
me. Good-bye, please don't you cry, 'cause we both

Fm
Ab/Eb
Db
Eb
know___ I'm not what___ you need.___ But
Chorus:
Ab
Fm
Db
Eb
Ab
Fm
I___ will al - ways_ love___ you.___ I___ will_
Db
Eb
Ab
Db/Ab
Ab
al - ways_ love___ you.___
Vince:
I hope_

Verse 3:
Eb/G
Fm
Ab/Eb
Dolly:
V.:
D.:
Both:
life I hope life treats you kind, treats you kind. and I hope you have all you dream
Db
Eb
Ab
Eb/G
Dolly:
Vince:
D.:
V.:
Both:
of. I wish you joy. Wish you joy and hap-pi - ness. and hap - pi - ness. But a -
Fm
Ab/Eb
Db
Eb
Bm7/E
E7
bove all this I wish you love. Oh, and

Chorus:
A
F♯m
D
E
A
F♯m
I will al - ways love you. I will al - ways love { you. / you. Yes. } I will al - ways love you. I will al - ways love you.
D
E
A
F♯m
D
E
rit. e dim.
N.C.
A(9)
A
mp
a tempo
rit.

(From Walt Disney's "BEAUTY AND THE BEAST")

BEAUTY AND THE BEAST

Lyrics by
HOWARD ASHMAN

Music by
ALAN MENKEN

Am7 B♭(9) C7sus C

friends, then some-bod - y bends un - ex-pect - ed - ly.

D G/D A/D D(9) D

Male: Just a lit-tle change. Small, to say the

3

Am7/D D7 Gmaj7 D(9)/F♯ Em7 D/A A7

least. Both a lit - tle scared, nei - ther one pre - pared. *Both:* Beau - ty and

D F♯m7

the Beast. Ev - er just the same.

8va

G
F♯m7
G(9)
Ev - er a sur - prise.
Ev - er as be -
F♯m7
Bm
C
fore, and ev - er just as sure as the sun will rise.
G/A
Asus
A
D(9)
G/D
A/D
D(9)
Male: Whoa, oh, oh. Woo oh.
cresc.
Em/D
F♯7/A♯
Bm
F♯m7
G(9)

Asus G/A A7/G F♯m7 G(9)

Both: Ev - er just the same. *Male:* Yeah, yeah. Ev - er a sur-

F♯m7 G(9) F♯m7

prise. *Both:* Ev - er as be - fore, *Female:* ev - er just as

Bm C C7/B♭ F/A C/D

sure *Both:* as the sun will rise. *Male:* Oh, oh, oh.

G C/G D/G G(9)

Female: Tale as old as time, tune as old

C/G
D/G
G
G/D
B7(♯9)
as song.
Both: Bit - ter sweet and strange, find - ing you can
Em
C
Dsus
D
E(9)
change, learn - ing you were wrong.
Male: Cer - tain as the
mf
A/E
B/E
E9
Bm7
E7
sun.
Female: (Cer - tain as the sun.)
Male: ris - ing in the East.
Female: Tale as old as
Amaj7
C♯m
F♯m7
E/B
B7
E
time,
Both: song as old as rhyme.
Beau - ty and the Beast.

C♯m
E/B
Amaj7
C♯m/G♯
F♯m7
E/B
B7
Female: Tale as old as time, Male: song as old as rhyme. Both: Beau - ty and the
rit.
E
A/E
B/E
E
Beast.
mp
A/E
B/E
Am/C
E/B
F♯/A♯
F♯m7(♭5)/A
E(9)/G♯
B/C♯
C♯7(♭9)
rit.
Freely
F♯m7
B13
E
Beau - ty and the Beast.
rit.

(I Wanna Take) FOREVER TONIGHT

Words and Music by
ANDY GOLDMARK and ERIC CARMEN

B♭m
G♭(9)
- er. I don't wan - na act tough, I just wan - na fall in love. As we move
Turn the light down low, make the world go slow. When I'm hold -
A♭(9)
D♭(9)
B♭m7
into the night, I get cra - zy thinking
- ing you to - night, it's so ea - sy. Noth-ing
D♭(9)
B♭m7
G♭(9)
how it's gon-na be with you ba - by. I don't wan - na play rough, I've been lov -
moves me like you do when you tease me. And to rush would be a crime, I just wan -
A♭(9)
Fm7
ing you e - nough, oh, ba - by.
na spend some time with you ba - by.
I wan-na take for -

Chorus:
Gb
Ab(9)
Fm7
ev - er to - night, wan - na stay in this mo - ment for - ev -
Bbm
Db/Ab
Ebm7
Gb
Ab(9)
Fm7
- er. I'm gon - na give you all the love that I've got. I wan - na take for -
Gb
Ab(9)
Fm7
ev - er to - night, fill you up, fill you up with
Bbm
Db/Ab
Ebm7
Fm7
love. When we close the door all I need

Gb
F7/A
Bbm
Db/Ab
Ebm7
is in your eyes.
Whoa,
I wan - na take for -
1.
Ab(9)
Db(9)
Bbm7
ev - er to - night.
Db(9)
Bbm7
2.
Ab(9)
2. Touch my lips,
ev - er.
Bridge:
A
G#m7
F#m7
F#m7/B
And when I'm here be - side you,
wan - na see what drives you out of your mind.

E
E/G♯
A
G♯m7
E♭m7
G♭
Oh, ba - by, I nev-er want to leave, I on-ly wan-na be with you, 'cause I
A♭(9)
Fm7
love how you feel, your love is so real. I on - ly know I wan-na take for -
Chorus:
G♭
A♭(9)
Fm7
ev - er to - night, wan - na stay in this mo - ment for - ev -
B♭m
D♭/A♭
E♭m7
G♭
A♭(9)
Fm7
- er. I'm gon - na give you all the love that I've got. I wan - na take for -

G♭
A♭(9)
Fm7
ev - er to - night,
wan - na stay in this mo - ment for - ev -
B♭m
D♭/A♭
E♭m7
G♭
A♭(9)
- er.
I'm gon - na give you all the love that I've got.
'Cause I can't live with - out
D♭(9)
B♭m
D♭(9)
B♭m
you.
D♭(9)
B♭m
D♭(9)
B♭m
Repeat ad lib. and fade

I'M YOUR ANGEL

Words and Music by
R. KELLY

C(9)
G
C/E
No riv - er's too wide for you to make it a - cross. All you have
You have ev - 'ry - thing and you're still lone - ly. It don't have
F
Gsus
G
E/G♯
to do is be - lieve it when you pray. And
to be this way. Let me show you a bet - ter day. And
Am
E7/G♯
C/G
D9/F♯
then you will see, the morn-ing will come, and ev - er - y day will be bright as the sun.
then you will see, the morn-ing will come, and all of your days will be bright as the sun. So
Dm7
C(9)/E
F/A
G/B
All of your fears, cast them on me. I just want you to see.
all of your fears, just cast them on me. How can I make you see?
I'll be your

Chorus:
C
Am7
Gsus
G
C/E
cloud up in the sky. I'll be your shoulder when you cry. I'll hear your
F
F/A
Gsus
G
F/A
G/B
voic - es when you call me. I am your an - gel. And when all
C
Am7
Gsus
G
C/E
hope is gone, I'm here. No mat - ter how far you are, I'm near. It makes no
F
F/A
Gsus
G
dif - fer - ence who you are, I am your an - gel. I'm your
3

1.

F C

an - gel.

2.

Bridge:

F C

an - gel. And when it's time to face the storm,

Cmaj7 Em7 Dm7 C Cmaj7

I'll be right by your side. Grace will keep us safe and warm,

F Em7 Dm7 Am7 E7/G♯

and I know we will sur - vive. And when it seems as if your end

C/G
D9/F♯
F
is draw - ing near,
don't you dare give up the fight.
Just put your
(The end is draw - ing near.)
G
E♭m7/A♭
N.C.
trust be - yond the sky.
I'll be your
Chorus:
D
Bm7
Asus
A
D/F♯
cloud up in the sky.
I'll be your shoul - der when you cry.
I'll hear your

G
G/B
Asus
A
G/B
A/C♯
voic - es when you call ___ me. I am your an - gel. And when all ___
D
Bm7
Asus
A
D/F♯
hope is gone, _ I'm here. _ No mat - ter how far you are, ___ I'm near. ___ It makes no ___
G
G/B
Asus
A
Repeat ad lib. and fade
dif - fer - ence who you are, ___ I am your an - gel. I'll be your

IN ANOTHER'S EYES

Words and Music by
BOBBY WOOD, JOHN PEPPARD
and GARTH BROOKS

G
1.
D
A7sus
2.
D
Em7
D/F♯
oth-er's eyes,
yeah,
yeah.
2. In an -
In an -
Chorus:
G
D/F♯
A7sus
A7
oth-er's eyes,
I'm a - fraid that I can't see
this pic-ture per - fect por-trait that they paint
D
G
Bm7
of me. They don't re-al-ize,
and I pray they nev-er do.
'Cause ev -
Em7
D/F♯
A7sus
A7
To Coda
'ry time I look, I'm see-in' you
in an -

Verse 3:
G/D
D
C/G
G
D
oth- er's eyes.
Whoa.
3. In an - oth - er's eyes,
star- in'
A7sus
A7
D
G
back at me,
I see a sink - ing soul
try- ing des - p'rate - ly
to turn the tide
D
A7sus
A7
G
be- fore it dies
in an - oth- er's eyes,
yeah,
Bridge:
D
Bm
A/C♯
D
Em7
D/F♯
G
yeah.
And what they don't see,
Lord, is kill - ing me.
It's a

Verse 2:
In another's eyes, I can do no wrong.
He believes in me and his faith is strong.
I'd never fall or even compromise,
In another's eyes.
(To Chorus:)

COUNT ON ME

Words and Music by
BABYFACE, WHITNEY HOUSTON
and MICHAEL HOUSTON

Em7
F#
Bm
Em11
7fr
D/F#
Don't be a - fraid.
Please be - lieve me when I say,
Em9/A
Dmaj7
Em7
count on.
I can see it's hurt - ing you.
Dmaj7/F#
Em7
Dmaj7
Em7
I can feel your pain.
It's hard to see the sun - shine through the
Am9
5fr
D7
Gmaj9
A7/G
rain.
I know some-times it seems as if it's

F#m7
Bm7
2fr
Em7
nev - er gon - na end, __ but you'll get through it, just
Em9/A
Chorus:
D
Em7
don't __ give in. 'Cause you can count on me __ through thick _ and thin, a friend -
D/F#
Gmaj13
3fr
D/A
A/G
- ship that __ will nev - er end. When you __ are weak, __ I will _ be strong, _
D(9)/F#
G(9)
Dmaj7/F#
Bm
help - ing you __ to car - ry on. ______ Call on me, _ I will _ be there. _

Em7
F#
Bm
Em11
7fr
D/F#
To Coda I
To Coda II
Don't be a - fraid. Please be - lieve me when I say,
Em7/A
D
Em7
count on, you can count on me. Ah,
D/F#
Em7
D
Em7
Am7
D7
yes you can. I know
Bridge:
Gmaj9
A/G
F#m7
Bm
some - times it seems as if we're stand-in' all a - lone. But

Em7
Em7/A
D.S. % al Coda I
we'll get through it, 'cause love won't let us fold.
Coda I
Em9/A
G/B
F#7/C#
count on. There's a place in - side of all of us where our
Bm/D
B7/D#
Em
F#7
faith in love be - gins. You should reach to find the truth in love, the
Bm
Em7
A/G
an - swer's there with - in. I know that life can make you feel it's much

F♯m7
Bm
Em7
Em7/A
D.S. 𝄋 al Coda II
hard-er than _ it real-ly is, ___ but we'll get through it, just don't, don't give _ in.
Coda II
F♯m/A Em7/A
count on, count on, count on, count on, count on, count on, count on
Dmaj7
Em7
Dmaj7
Em7
me. ___ Ah, yes you can, _
Dmaj7
Em7
Dmaj7
know I can, oh yeah. _ count on me. __
__ sure you can, So glad I can _ count on me, __

From the Motion Picture "AN OFFICER AND A GENTLEMAN"

UP WHERE WE BELONG

Words by
WILL JENNINGS

Music by
BUFFY SAINTE-MARIE
and JACK NITZSCHE

Em7
A
road is long. There are
cresc.
D
D/F#
G
G/B
C
D/C
moun - tains in our way, but we climb a step ev - 'ry
mp
3
Chorus:
A
G/A
A
D
D/F#
G
Bm
day. Love lift us up where we be-long, where the
cresc.
f
Em
D/F#
C
G
A
D
D/F#
ea - gles cry on a moun - tain high. Love lift us up where we be-long,

G
Bm
Em
D/F♯
far from the world we know; up where the
1.
F♯/A♯
Bm
Gm
D
G/D
Gm/D
clear winds blow.
decresc.
2.
G/A
A
F
C/E
E♭
B♭/D
clear winds blow. Time goes by, no time to cry,
decresc.
mp
D♭
A♭/C
B♭
Fm7/B♭
E♭
life's you and I, a - live, to - day.
cresc. poco a poco
f

Eb Eb/G Ab Cm

Love lift us up where we be-long, where the

Fm Eb/G Db Ab Bb Eb Eb/G

ea - gles cry, on a moun - tain high. Love lift us up where we be-long

Repeat ad lib and fade

Ab Cm Fm Eb/G G/B Cm Abm

far from the world we know; where the clear winds blow.

Verse 2:
Some hang on to "used-to-be",
Live their lives looking behind.
All we have is here and now;
All our life, out there to find.
The road is long.
There are mountains in our way,
But we climb them a step every day.

BURNIN' THE ROADHOUSE DOWN

Words and Music by
RICK CARNES and STEVE WARINER

A6
The band is heat - in' up and giv - ing ev - 'ry - thing they've got.
er. One spark from that fid - dle bow could set this place on fire.
B9
E7
A6
Some - bod - y check the ex - its in case a fire breaks out.
It's so cool to be here in the hot - test place in town.
A7
D7
We're packed in tight, Feels so right, it's Sat - ur - day night, and we're burn - in' the road - house down.
A6
F#7
B9
E7
N.C.
We're burn - in' it down.
Chorus:
D7

* Optional Instrumental solo in cue notes.

A6
A7
D7
A6
(Instrumental solo . . .
F♯7
B7
E7
A6
A7
D7
A6
. . . continue ad lib. solo . . .
F♯7
B7
E7
A6
D.S. 𝄋 al Coda
2. Yeah, it's a mob_
. . . end solo)
𝄌 Coda
A6
down.
They'll_ be sift - in' through the ash -

A7
D7
D♯dim7
es
when Sun - day rolls a - round.
But
A6
A7
F♯7
B9
E7
it's al - right, it's Sat - ur - day night and we're burn - in' the road - house
A6
down.
D7
A6
A♭
G
F♯
B9
F7
E7
A6

SOMEWHERE OUT THERE
(From "An American Tail")

Words and Music by
JAMES HORNER, BARRY MANN
and CYNTHIA WEIL

Dm7 C/E F Gsus G C(add9) Cmaj7/E
lov - ing me to - night. Some - where out
C/F F/G C(add9) C/E F
there some - one's say - ing a prayer that
Dm7 G/F Em7 Am Dm7 C/E F/G
we'll find one a - noth - er in that big some - where out
C F G/F F G/F
there. And e - ven though I know how ve - ry far a - part we are it

Fmaj7
G/F
F
G/F
helps to think_ we might_ be wish - in' on the same_bright - star. And
Ab
Bb/Ab
Ab
Bb/Ab
when the night_ wind starts to sing a lone - some lul - la - by it
Ab
Bb/Ab
G
helps to think we're sleep - ing un - der - neath the same big sky.
poco rit.
a tempo
C
Cmaj7/E
Fmaj9
F/G
To Coda
C
C/E
Some - where out there if love can see us

F
Dm7
G/F
Em7
Am7
F
3
through, then we'll be to - geth - er some-where out there, out
G
C
D/C
C
D/C
where dreams come true.
C/B♭
B♭maj7
Am/B♭
D/E
A
C♯m7
A/D
D/E
A
A/C♯
D
D+
D6
A/C♯
3

Bm7 Dmaj7 C♯m F♯m7 Bm7 C♯m D/E A
D.S. al Coda
And
CODA
C C/E F Dm G/F
love can see us through, then we'll be to-
(love can see us through)
Em7 Am F G
geth - er some-where out there, out where dreams come
poco rit.
use pedal
C Cmaj7/E C/F G7sus C(add9)
true.
a tempo
rit.

HOW 'BOUT US

Words and Music by
DANA WALDEN

Chorus:
B♭
Some peo-ple are made for each oth - er;
mf
Cm/B♭
some peo-ple can love one an - oth - er for life;
Cm7-5/B♭
how 'bout
B♭
us?
Some peo-ple can hold it to - geth - er;
Cm/B♭
man - age through all kinds of weath - er;
Cm7-5/B♭
but
can

1. B♭
Cm7-5/B♭
B♭
Cm7-5/B♭
D.S.
𝄋
we?
(Bkgr.) Ooh,
ooh,
ooh.
2. B♭
Cm7-5/B♭
we?
(Bkgr.) How 'bout us, how 'bout us ba - by? How 'bout us, how 'bout us ba - by?
B♭
Cm7-5/B♭
Gm
How 'bout us, how 'bout us ba - by, ooh?
(Lead:) Are we gon - na
Dm
Fm7
make it girl, or are we gon - na drift, and drift, and drift to - geth-er?

Verse 2:
Now don't you get me wrong,
'Cause I'm not trying now to end it all;
It's just that I have seen.
Too many lover's hearts lose their dream.
(To Chorus:)

HOUSE OF LOVE

Words and Music by
GREG BARNHILL, KENNY GREENBERG
and WALLY WILSON

D♭
Fm7
G♭maj7
bout it, some-times life is fun - ny. You think you're in your dark - est hour when the
Amaj7
B
D♭
D♭maj7
Fm7
lights are com-in' on in the house of love.
G♭maj7
A♭
Verse:
B♭m
Oh! 1. You've been up all night
A♭
B♭m
A♭
think-in' it was o - ver. He's been out of sight, at least for the mo-ment.

G♭maj7
A♭
But when some-thing this strong,
ooh,
gets a hold on you,
the odds are
E♭m7
G♭maj7/A♭
To Coda
nine - ty - nine to one
it's got a hold on him, too.
Chorus:
D♭
Fm7
Well, I bet you an - y a - mount of mon - ey he'll be com - in'
G♭maj7
B9
back to you.
Ooh, I know there ain't no doubt a -

Db
Fm7
Gbmaj7
bout it, some-times life is fun-ny. You think you're in your dark - est hour when the
Amaj7
B
Db
lights are com-in' on in the house of love. When the
Amaj7
B
1.
Db
D.S. 𝄋
2.
Db
D.S. 𝄋 al Coda
lights are com-in' on in the house of love. of love.
Coda
Chorus:
Eb
Gm7
Well, I bet you an-y a-mount of mon-ey he'll be com-in'

Verse 2:
Now, when the house is dark and you're all alone inside,
You've gotta listen to your heart, put away your foolish pride.
Though the storm is breakin' and thunder shakes the walls,
There with a firm foundation ain't it never, never, never gonna fall.
(To Chorus:)

Verse 3:
Though the storm is breakin' and thunder shakes the walls,
There with a firm foundation ain't it never, never, never gonna fall.
(To Chorus:)

ON MY OWN

Words and Music by
CAROLE BAYER SAGER and BURT BACHARACH

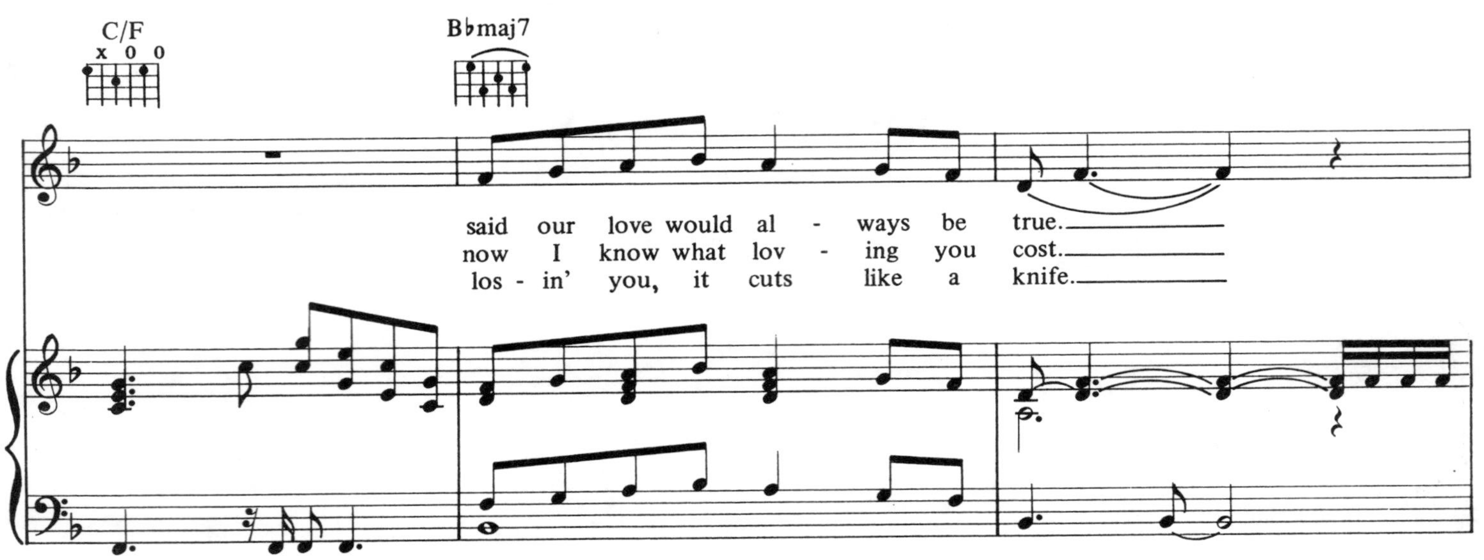
C/F
Bbmaj7
said our love would al - ways be true.
now I know what lov - ing you cost.
los - in' you, it cuts like a knife.

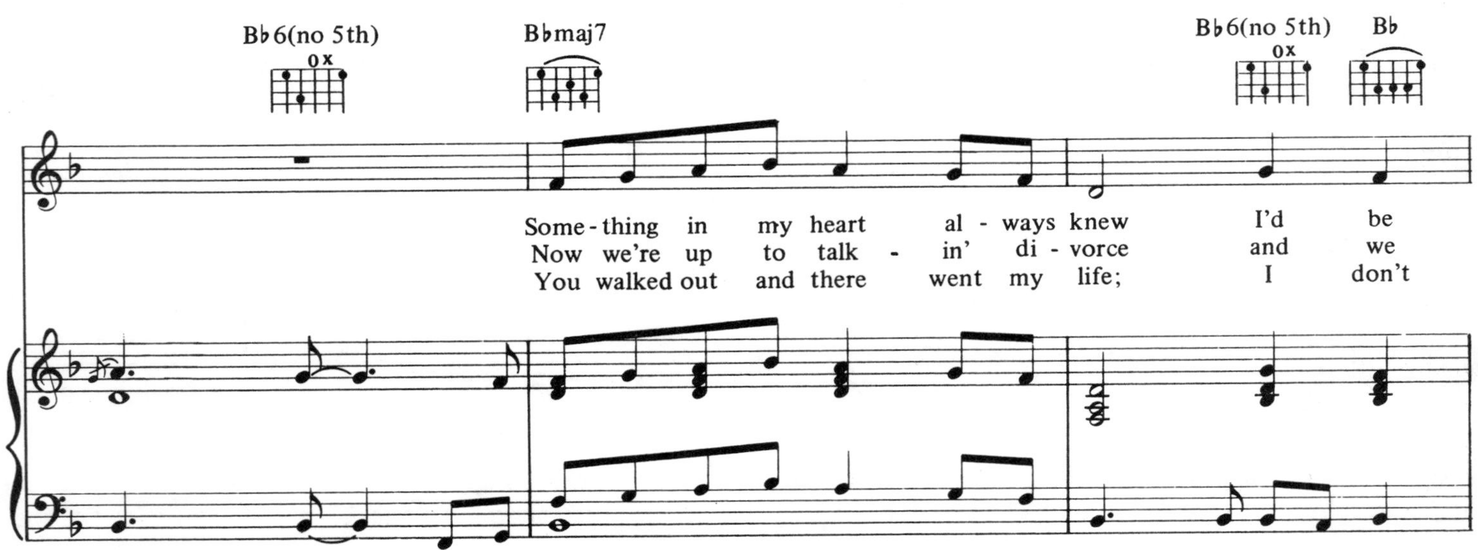
Bb6(no 5th)
Bbmaj7
Bb6(no 5th)
Bb
Some-thing in my heart al - ways knew I'd be
Now we're up to talk - in' di - vorce and we
You walked out and there went my life; I don't

F(addG)/C
To Coda
ly - ing here be - side you.
were - n't e - ven mar - ried.
want to live with - out you.
On my
On my
On my

Gm7/C
F(addG)/C
own, on my own,
own, once a - gain,
own, on my own,
on my own.
one more
on my
1.
Gm7/C
2.Gm7/C
F
time. By my - self;

F(no 3rd)
B♭maj7
C/B♭
C
no one said it was eas - y,
F
F(no 3rd)
B♭maj7
but it once was so eas - y.
Gm7
3fr.
Well, I be-lieved in love, now here
Am7
Dm7
I stand;
I won-der why

Gm7/C
Vocal ad lib
I'm on my own.
(Group) On my
F(addG)/C
Gm7/C
D.S. al Coda
own,
on my own.
Repeat and fade (vocal ad lib on repeats)
Coda
Gm7/C
F(addG)/C
own,
on my own,
on my
Gm7/C
F(addG)/C
F6(no 5th)/C
Vocal ad lib
own,
by my - self.
(Group) On my

From the Motion Picture "THE MIRROR HAS TWO FACES"

I FINALLY FOUND SOMEONE

Words and Music by
BARBRA STREISAND, MARVIN HAMLISCH,
R.J. LANGE and BRYAN ADAMS

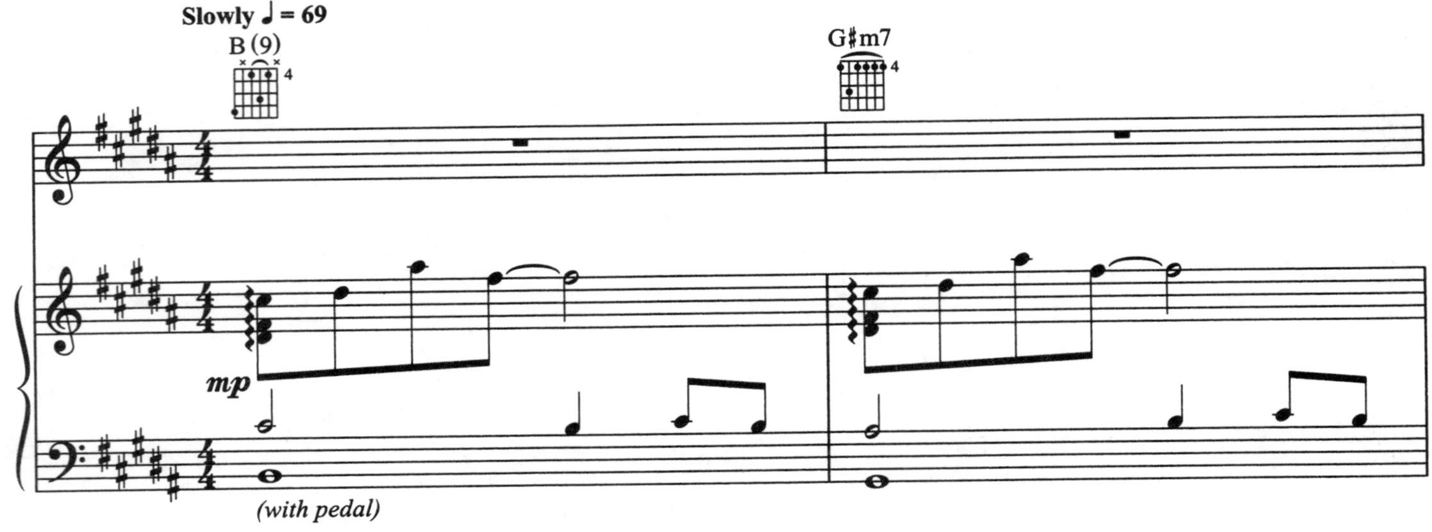

Emaj9
Em6
I fi-n'lly found the one__ that makes me feel com-plete.
B(9)
G♯m7
It start-ed o - ver cof - fee, we start-ed out as friends.
C♯m7/F♯
It's fun-ny how, from sim-ple things,_ the best things be - gin.___
A♭(9)
Fm7
___ This time, it's dif-f'rent, it's all be-cause of you.__

D♭maj9
D♭m6
It's bet-ter than it's ev - er been
'cause we can talk it { through.
through, yeah.
A♭(9)
Fm7
My fa-v'rite line was, "Can I call you some - time?"
D♭maj9
D♭m6
It's all you had to say to take my breath a - way.
Chorus:
F(9)
mf
This is it! Oh, I fi - n'lly

B♭maj9
B♭m6
F(9)
found some - one, some - one to share my life. I fi - n'lly
B♭maj9
B♭m6
F(9)
found the one to be with ev - 'ry night. 'Cause what -
A7sus
A7
Dm
D♭
ev - er I do, it's just got to be you. My
F/C
B♭/C
life has just be - gun, I fi - n'lly found some - one.

F(9)
Dm7
Ooh, some - one,
I fi - n'lly found some - one.
B♭maj9
F/G
Ooh,
Verse:
C(9)
Am7
I did - n't mind.
Ba - by, that's fine,
Did I keep you wait - ing?
I a - pol - o - gize.
Fmaj9
Fm6
just to know you were mine.
I will wait for - ev - er just to know you were mine.
You know,

C(9)
Am7
Are you sure it looks right?
Is-n't it too tight?
I love your hair,
I love what you wear.
Fmaj9
Fm6
I can't wait for the rest of my life!
Well, you're ex-cep-tion-al!
Chorus:
G♭(9)
This is it!
Oh,
I fi-n'lly
C♭maj9
C♭m6
G♭(9)
found some-one,
some-one to share my life.
I fi-n'lly

C♭maj9
C♭m6
G♭(9)
found the one_ to be with ev - 'ry_ night._ 'Cause what -
B♭7sus
B♭7
E♭m
ev - er I do,_ it's just got to be you.
D
G♭/D♭
Oh_ yeah, my life has just_ be - gun,_ I fi - n'lly
A♭m7/D♭
E♭7sus
E♭7
found some - one._ And what -

A♭m7
G♭/B♭
ev - er I do, it's just got to be you. Ooh, my
A♭m7/D♭
life has just be - gun, I fi - n'lly
G♭(9)
C♭maj9
found some - one.
G♭(9)

IF YOU SEE HIM/IF YOU SEE HER

Words and Music by
TERRY McBRIDE, JENNIFER KIMBALL
and TOMMY LEE JAMES

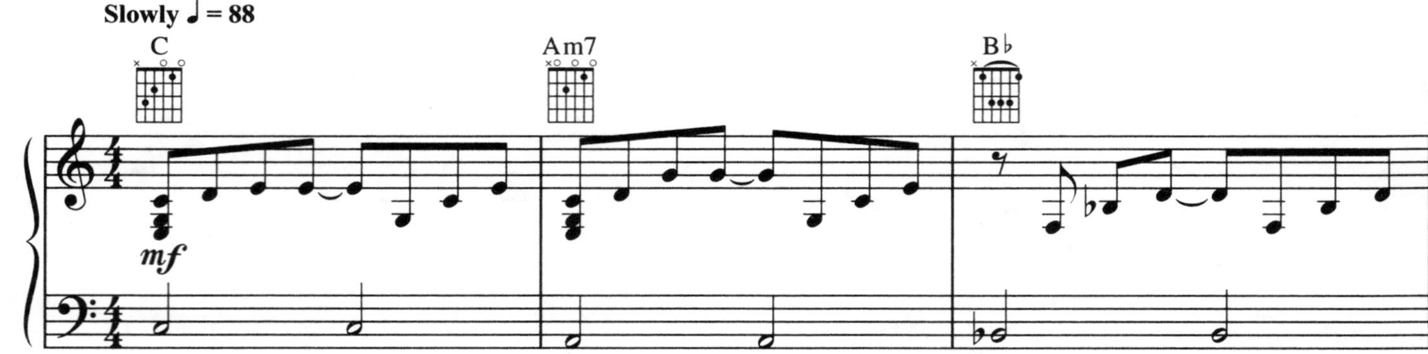

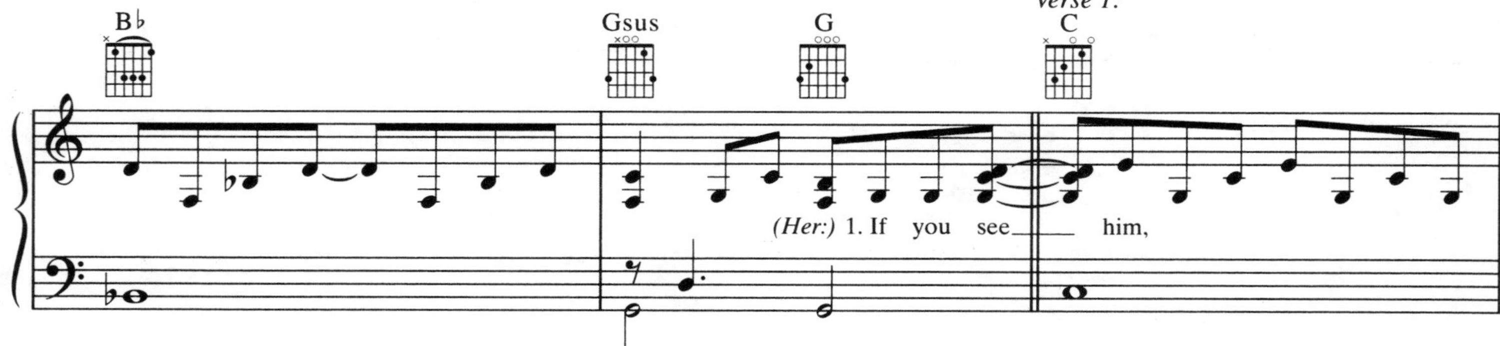

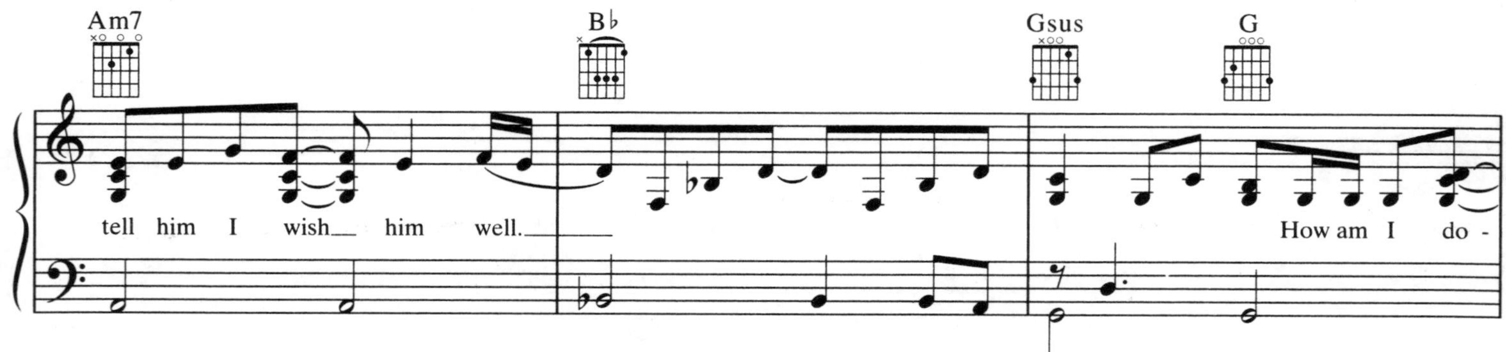

If You See Him/If You See Her - 5 - 1

C
Am7
B♭
ing? Well, some-times it's hard to tell.
Gsus
G
F(9)
G
I still miss him more than ev - er, but
C
F
Dm
please don't say a word if you see him,
G
C
Dsus
D
if you see him.
(Him:) 2. If you
Verses 2 & 3:
G
Em7
F
see her, tell her I'm do - in' fine.
3. See additional lyrics

Dsus
D
G
Em7
And if you want to,
say that I think of her
F
Dsus
D
C (9)
from time to time.
Ask her if she ev -
D
G
C
G/B
er won - ders where we both went wrong if you
Am7
To Coda
D
G
see her, if you see her.
Bridge:
D/F♯
Em7
C
(Him:) Whoa, I, I still want her. (Her:) And

D
C
G
D
D/F♯
I still need him so.
(Both:) Whoa,
I don't know why we let each oth - er go.
Em7
C
Am7
C
D
G
D/F♯
Em7
C
D
C
D/F♯
D
Em7
C
Am7
C
D
D.S. al Coda
(Him:) 3. If you

Verse 3:
(Him:) If you see her, tell her the light's still on for her.
(Her:) Nothing's changed, deep down the fire still burns for him.
(Both:) And even if it takes forever, say I'll still be here.
(Her:) If you see him.
(Him:) If you see her.

TIME TO SAY GOODBYE
(Con Te Partiró)

Lyrics by LUCIO QUARANTOTTO
English Lyrics by FRANK PETERSON

Music by
FRANCESCO SARTORI

Gsus
G
Dsus
D
C/E
Em
C
D
so - le se non ci sei tu con me, con me.
G
D/F♯
Em7
C
D
Su le fi - ne - stre mo-stra_a tut-ti_il mio cuo-re che hai ac - ce - so
G
D/F♯
Em7
C
D
chiu - di den-tro me la lu - ce che hai_incon-tra - to per stra - da.
Chorus:
G
D
Em7
C
G
D
Time to say good - bye. Pa - e - si che non ho

Em7
C
G
C
D7
G
D
mai ve-du-to_e vis-su-to con te a-des-so sì li vi-vrò con te par-ti-
Em7
C
G
D
Em7
C
To Coda
rò su na-vi per ma-ri che io lo so no no non e-si-sto-no
G
C
D7
Verse 2:
C/D
più con te io li vi-vrò.
2. Quan-do sei lon-ta-na so-gno_al-l'o-riz-zon-te_e man-can le pa-
Gsus
G
C
D
C
D
C
D
Em
ro - le, e io sì lo so che sei con me, con me. Tu mia lu-na tu sei qui con me

C/E
D
C
D
C/E
D/F♯
D.S. 𝄋 al Coda
mi - o so - le tu sei qui con me, con me, con me, con me.
Coda
G
C
D7
Tag:
A
E
più con te io li ri vi - vrò con te par - ti -
F♯m7
D
A
E
F♯m7
D
rò su na - vi per ma - ri che io lo so no no non e - si - sto - no
A
D
E7
A
E
F♯m7
D
più con te io li ri - vi - vrò con te par - ti - rò.

English literal translation:
Verse 1:
When I'm alone,
I dream of the horizon
And words fail me.
There is no light
In a room where there is no sun.
And there is no sun if you're not here
With me, with me.
From every window,
Unfurl my heart,
The heart that you have won.
Into me you've poured the light,
The light that you've found
By the side of the road.

Chorus:
Time to say goodbye.
Places that I've never seen
Or experienced with you,
Now I shall.
I'll sail with you upon ships across the seas,
Seas that exist no more.
It's time to say goodbye.

Verse 2:
When you're far away,
I dream of the horizon
And words fail me.
And of course, I know that you're with me,
With me.
You, my moon, you are with me.
My sun, you're here with me,
With me, with me, with me.

Chorus:
Time to say goodbye.
Places that I've never seen
Or experienced with you,
Now I shall.
I'll sail with you upon ships across the seas,
Seas that exist no more,
I'll revive them with you.

Tag:
I'll go with you upon ships across the seas,
Seas that exist no more,
I'll revive them with you.
I'll go with you,
I'll go with you.

From the Miramax Motion Picture "Music Of The Heart"

MUSIC OF MY HEART

Words and Music by
DIANE WARREN

F♯7sus
F♯7
B
B/D♯
G♯m7
done for my soul.
You'll nev - er know the gift you've
see - ing me through.
You were the song that al - ways
E
B/D♯
give - en me.
I'll car - ry it with me.
made me sing.
I'm sing - ing this for you.
C♯m7
B/D♯
Through the days a - head, I think of days be - fore, when you made me
Ev - 'ry - where I go, I think of where I've been and of the

Amaj9
C♯m7/F♯
hope for some - thing bet - ter and made me reach for some - thing more.
one who knew me bet - ter than an - y - one ev - er will a - gain.
You taught me to run,
Chorus:
B
F♯/A♯
C♯m7
you taught me to fly, helped me to free the me in - side. Helped me hear the
E
B/D♯
C♯m7
C♯m7/F♯
mu - sic of my heart. Helped me hear the mu - sic of my heart. You o - pened my
B
F♯/A♯
Amaj9
eyes, you o - pened the door to some - thing I've nev - er known be - fore. And your

1.

C♯m7 C♯m7/F♯ A2

love is the mu - sic of___ my heart.

2.

C♯m7 C♯m7/F♯

love is the mu - sic of___ my

Bridge:

E F♯

heart. What you taught_ me, on - ly

E/G♯ F♯/A♯ B

your love could ev - er teach___ me. You got through where no one could reach___ me be - fore.___

(Be -

E C♯m7

fore.___)

Coz you al - ways saw_ in me_____ all the best_

B/D♯
Amaj9
C♯m7/F♯
that I could be. It was you who set me free. You taught me to run,
B
F♯/A♯
C♯m7
you taught me to fly, helped me to free the me in - side. Helped me hear the
E
B/D♯
C♯m7
B/D♯
C♯m7/F♯
E♭m7/A♭
mu - sic of my heart. Helped me hear the mu - sic of my heart. You taught me to run,
Chorus:
D♭
A♭/C
E♭m7
you taught me to fly, helped me to free the me in - side. Helped me hear the

G♭
D♭/F
E♭m7
D♭
A♭/C
E♭m7/A♭
music of my heart. Helped me hear the music of my heart. You opened my
D♭
A♭/C
C♭maj9
eyes, you opened the door to something I've never known before. And your
E♭m7
E♭m7/A♭
C♭2
love is the music of my heart,
rit.
D♭
is the music of my heart.

MAYBE NOT TONIGHT

Words and Music by
KEITH STEGALL and DAN HILL

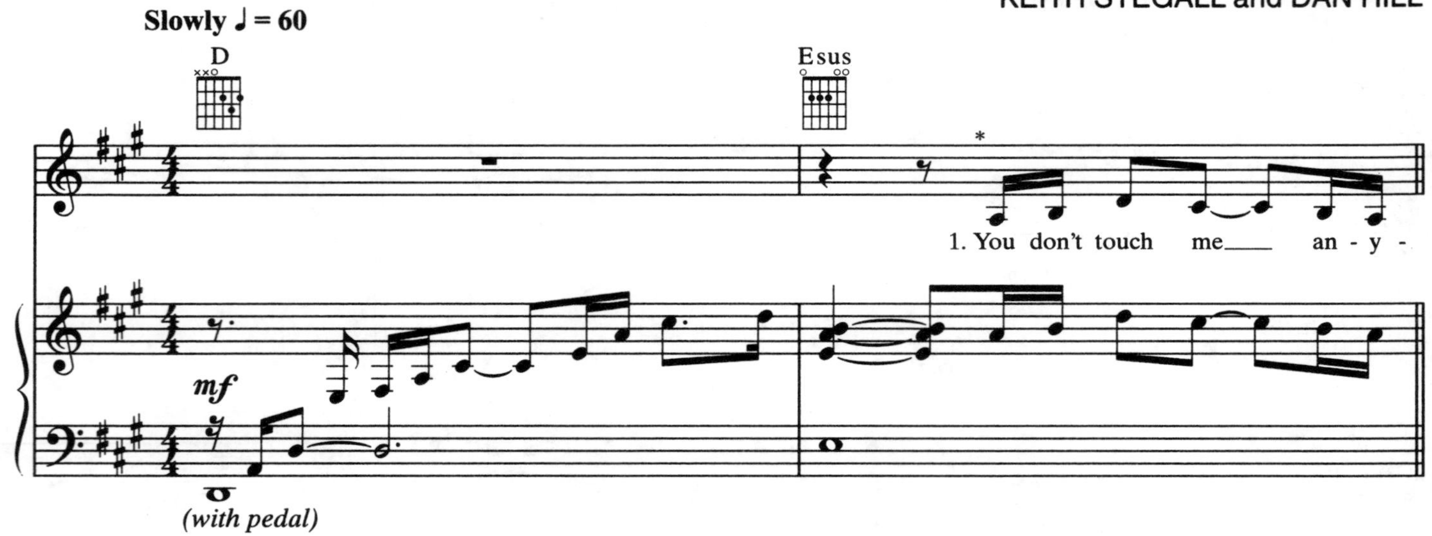

* Vocals written at pitch.

Esus
E
Esus
E
Your si-lence cuts me__ like a ra-zor.
I'm gon-na
C#m7
D
C#m7
F#m7
Bm7
leave you,__ may-be some-day__ soon,__ when I can give up this fight,__
1.
Esus
D
Esus
but may-be__ not__ to-night.__
2. We don't talk much__ an-y-
2.
Esus
A
but may-be not__ to-night.
Can you just
cresc.

Chorus:
E/D
D
E/D
D
hold me in your arms so deep? Wan-na feel you breath-
f
C♯m7
F♯m7
G
in' on my skin. We fell out of love.
Bm7
Esus
Fsus
We can fall back in. Female: 3. You nev-er look at me that
dim.
Verse 3:
B♭
way. Male: So man-y times I've longed to say. F: You used to brush the hair back
mf

F/E♭
E♭
from my face.
M: God, how I miss those days.
You used to make me feel like
Cm7
some - one.
F: Tell me, where did we go wrong?
M: You were my best friend, my one and
Fsus
F
on - ly love.
F: You're still the on - ly one.
Just as I'm
Dm7
E♭
Dm7
Gm7
Cm7
leav - in' you,
you walk in the room.
I see the flick-er in your eyes.

Fsus
B♭
Both: We say, "May - be not to - night."
Can you just
cresc.
Chorus:
F/E♭
E♭
F/E♭
E♭
hold me in your arms so deep? Wan - na feel you breath -
f
Dm7
Gm7
in' on my skin.
F: We fell
A♭
Cm
out of love.
M: How did we fall out of love?
Both: May-be we can fall
dim.

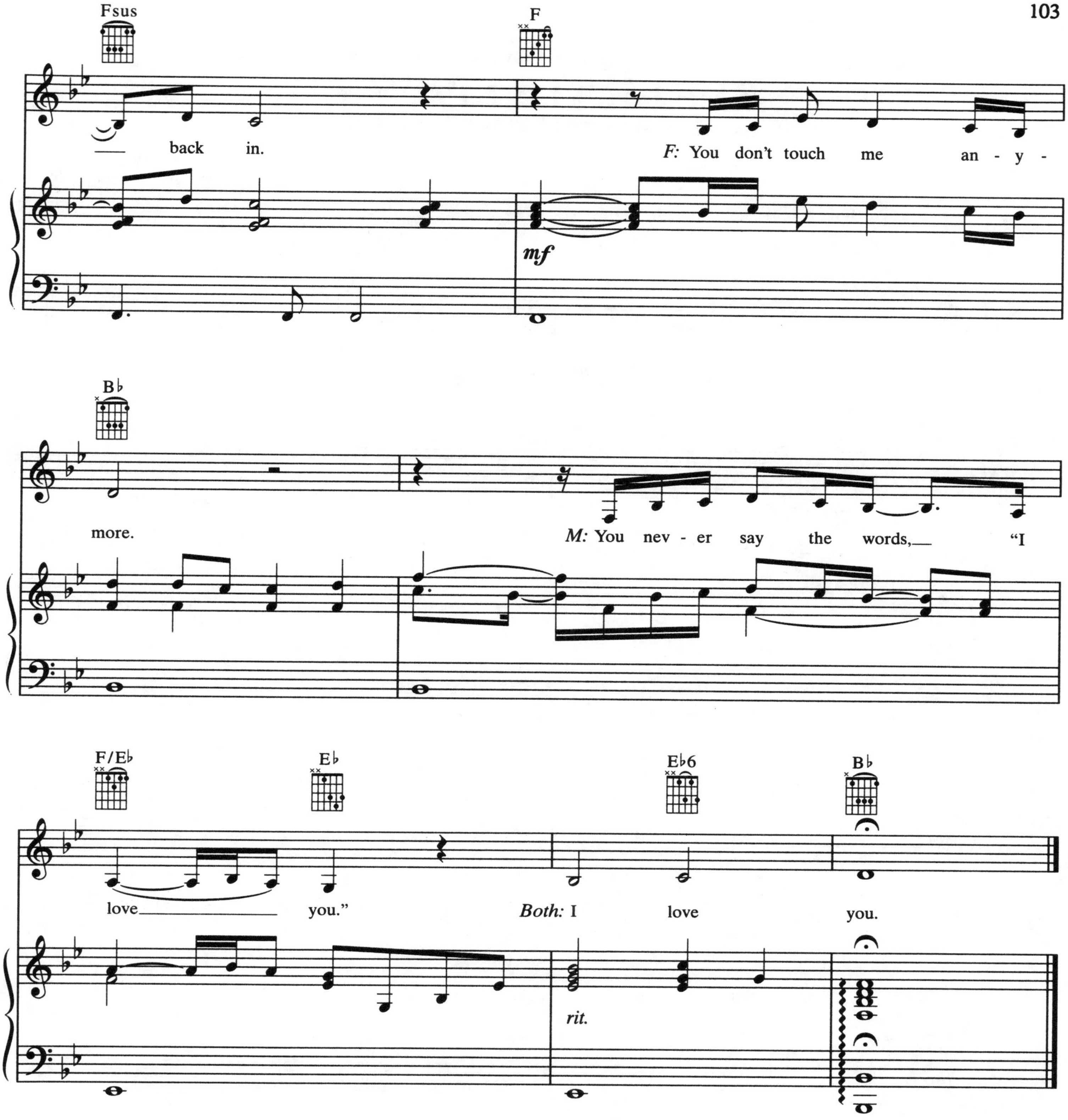
Fsus
F
back in.
F: You don't touch me an - y -
mf
B♭
more.
M: You nev - er say the words, "I
F/E♭
E♭
E♭6
B♭
love you."
Both: I love you.
rit.

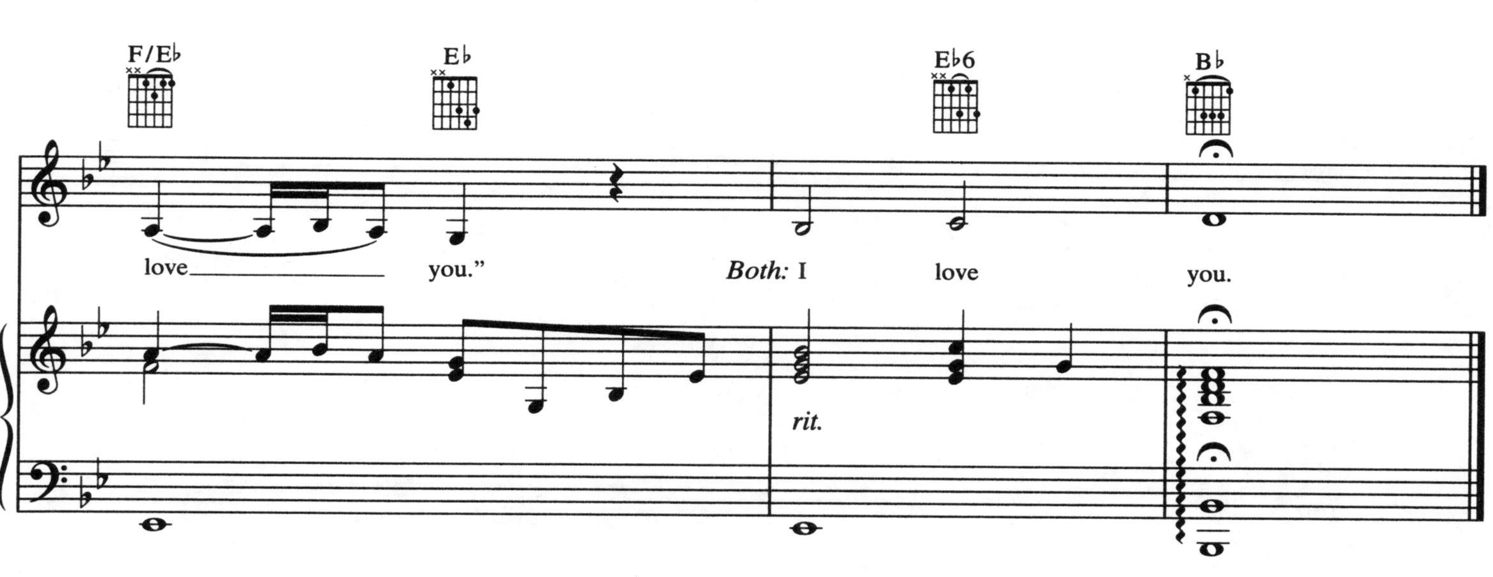

Verse 2:
We don't talk much anymore,
Not the same way we used to.
Whenever I reach out to hold you,
You turn away.
What am I supposed to do?
I'm gonna say good-bye when the moment's right.
Like an eagle I will fly, but maybe not tonight.
(To Chorus:)

Columbia Pictures Presents A New Vision Production "WHITE NIGHTS"

SEPARATE LIVES

(Love Theme from "White Nights")

By
STEPHEN BISHOP

C♯m7
3fr.
G♯m
4fr.
A
leav - ing so soon,
and that you miss me some - times
AaddB
F♯m7/A
B7/D♯
Esus4
when you're a - lone in your room.
Do I feel lone - ly too?
E
EaddF♯
G♯m+5
C♯m7
4fr.
Am9/C
sfz
f
You have no right
E
B7/A
E
F♯m7-5/E
to ask me how I feel.
You have no right

E F♯m7/A B7

to speak to me so kind.

A/C♯ G♯m/B F♯m/C♯ E/G♯ A Bm7sus4 B7

I can't go on just hold - ing on to ties.

C♯m7sus4 C♯m7 4fr. G♯m7 4fr. E/G♯ F♯m7

now that we're liv - ing

mf

B7sus4 2fr. E A/E

sep - 'rate lives.

E
A
C♯/G♯
4fr.
sfz
B
C7+5/B♭
D7/A
E
B7/A
Well, I held on__ to let__ you go__
f
E
F♯m7-5/E
E
__ and if you lost__ your love__ for me__
G♯m+5
F♯m7/B
A/C♯
G♯m/B
F♯m/C♯
E/G♯
__ will you nev-er let it show.__ There was no way__

A
B7sus4
2fr.
B7
C♯m7sus4
C♯m7
4fr.
G♯m7
4fr.
E/G♯
3
to com - pro - mise
so now we're
mf
F♯7
B7sus4
2fr.
E
liv - ing
sep - 'rate lives.
AaddB
G♯m7+5
F♯7
C♯m7/G♯
4fr.
AaddB/E
Ooo, it's so ty - pi - cal love leads to is - o - la - tion.
mp
F♯m7
G♯m+5
A
So you build that wall,
yes, you build that wall
f

B7sus4
2fr.
C♯m7
4fr.
D9
4fr.
A6 B7sus4/G♯
and you make it strong-er.
Well, you have no right
ff
E
B7/A
E
F♯m7-5/E
3
to ask me how I feel.
You have no right
E
F♯m7/A
B7
to speak to me so kind.
A/C♯
G♯m
4fr.
F♯m7
E
A
Freely
Some-day I might
find my-self
subito mf

Bm7sus4
B7
E
G♯m7
3fr.
F♯m7
look - ing in — your eyes,
but for now we'll go on liv -
3
mp
B7
E
F♯m7
C♯m7
4fr.
Freely
ing sep - 'rate lives.
Yes, for now we'll go on
rit.
mf
F♯m7-5/C
B7-9
C♯m7
4fr.
AaddB
E
liv - ing sep - 'rate lives.
Ha ha ha
3
mf a tempo
AaddB/E
G♯m+5
F♯m7/A
B7sus4
2fr.
E
ha.
Ha ha ha — ha ha.
Sep - 'rate lives.
3
molto rit.

TOO MUCH, TOO LITTLE, TOO LATE

Words and Music by
NAT KIPNER and JOHN VALLINS

Too Much, Too Little, Too Late - 3 - 1

Fm6
Abm6
Cmaj7
Ebmaj7
To Coda
1.
Dm7/G
Fm7/Bb
We knew it had to end some - day,
So lit - tle left for you and me,
let's face it, why de - ny it's o - ver,
this way.
and it's
it's
2.
Dm7
Fm7
E7sus4
G7sus4
E7
G7
Fmaj7
Abmaj7
G/F
Bb/Ab
clear to see:
Too much, too lit - tle, too late to lie a - gain with you.
Too much, too lit - tle, too late to ev - er try a - gain.
Em7
Gm7
Em7/A
Gm7/C
A7
C7
Too much, too lit - tle, too late to try a - gain with you.
Too much, too lit - tle, too late. Let's end it be - ing friends.
Dm7
Fm7
Fm6
Abm6
We're in the mid - dle of end - ing some - thing that we knew was
Too much, too lit - tle too late. We knew it had to end. It's

1.
2.
C
Eb
Dm7
Fm7
E7
G7
Dm9/G
Fm9/Bb
D.S. al Coda
o - ver. It was o - ver. o - ver.
o - ver. It's
Repeat and fade
Coda
Dm7/G
Fm7/Bb
Fmaj7
Abmaj7
G/F
Bb/Ab
o - ver. Too much, too lit - tle, too late to ev - er try a - gain.
Repeat and fade
Em7
Gm7
Em7/A
Gm7/C
A7
C7
Dm7
Fm7
Too much, too lit - tle, too late. Let's end it be - ing friends. Too much, too lit - tle, too late. We knew
Fm6
Abm6
C
Eb
Dm7
Fm7
E7
G7
it had to end. And it's o - ver. It's o - ver.

TELL HIM

Words and Music by
LINDA THOMPSON, DAVID FOSTER
and WALTER AFANASIEFF

D♯/F𝄪
G♯m
Ooh, what if there's an - oth - er one he's
2. See additional lyrics
mf
D♯m/F♯
Emaj7
F♯/E
think-ing of? May - be he's in love. I'd feel like a
D♯m7
G♯m7
C♯m7
B
fool. Life can be so cruel. I don't know what to do.
Emaj7
Barbra:
I've been there, with my heart out in my

D♯m7
G♯m7
D
hand.
But what you must un - der - stand,
you can't let the
A/C♯
E
chance to love him pass you by.
Chorus:
A
F♯m7
Both:
Tell him, tell him that the sun and moon rise
D6
Bm7(♭5)/E
E
A
in his eyes. Reach out to him and whis - per

F♯m7
Dmaj7
Celine:
ten - der words so soft and sweet. I'll hold him__ close to feel his heart_ beat.___
1.
Bm7/E
E
A
Barbra:
___ Love__ will be__ the gift you give your - self.__
2.
Bm7/E
A
Celine:
___ Love will be the gift you give your - self.___
Bridge:
F
B♭maj7
Em7
C/E
Dm7
G7/B
___ Love is light_ that sure - ly glows in the hearts of those who know. It's a stead - y flame_ that

C
A♭
D♭maj7
Cm7
Fm7
Barbra:
Celine:
grows. Feed the fire with all the pas-sion you can show. To-night,
B♭m7
A♭/C
D♭maj7
E♭/F
Fm7
Barbra:
love will as-sume it's place. This mem-'ry time can-not e-rase.
B♭m7
A♭/C
Fsus
F
Both:
Your faith will lead love where it has to go.
rall.
B♭
Gm7
E♭6
Tell him, tell him that the sun and moon rise in his eyes. Reach
a tempo

Verse 2:
(Barbra:)
Touch him with the gentleness you feel inside. (*C:* I feel it.)
Your love can't be denied.
The truth will set you free.
You'll have what's meant to be.
All in time, you'll see.
(Celine:)
I love him, *(B:* Then show him.*)*
Of that much I can be sure. *(B:* Hold him close to you.)
I don't think I could endure
If I let him walk away
When I have so much to say.
(To Chorus:)

MY KIND OF WOMAN/MY KIND OF MAN

Words and Music by
VINCE GILL

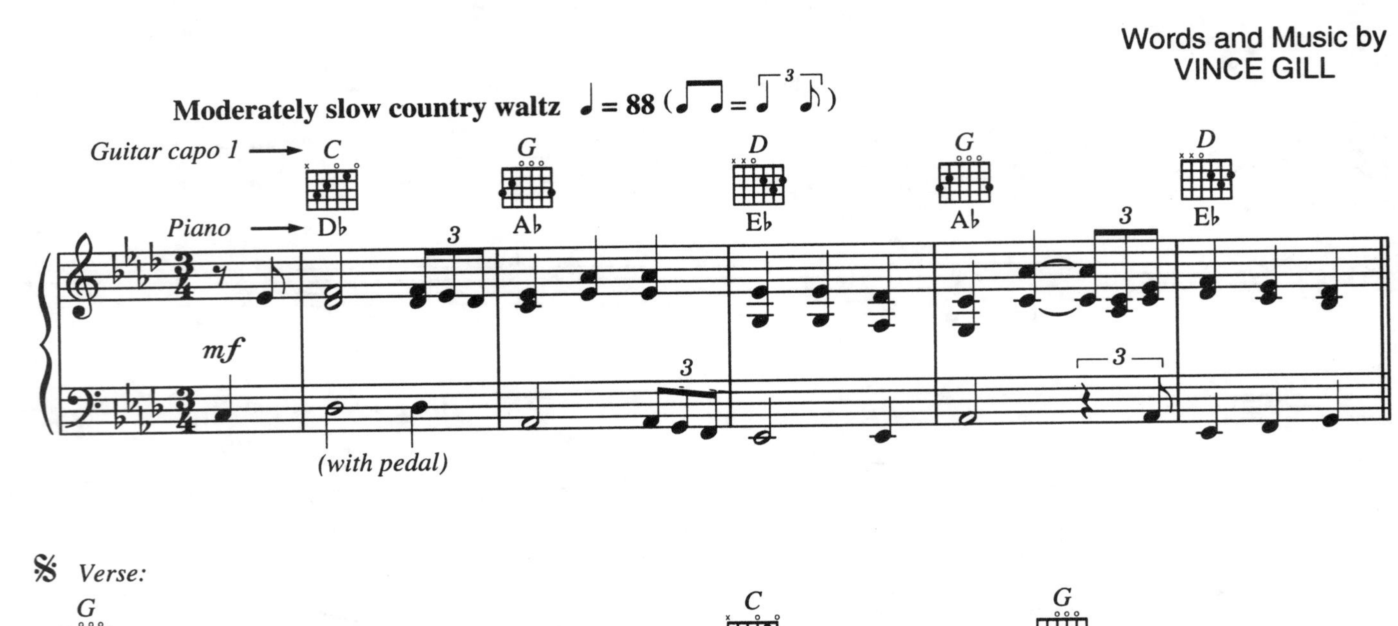

*Female vocal sung one octave lower.

Chorus:
C
Db
G
Ab
my kind of wom - an, you're my kind of man.
A7
Bb7
A match made in heav - en by God's gen - tle
D
Eb
C
Db
hand. I'll love you for - ev - er; to -
G
Ab
Male:
C
Db
geth - er we'll stand. You're my kind of

1.
D.S.
G
Ab
D
Female: Eb
G
Ab
D
Eb
wom - an. You're my kind of man.

2.
D
Eb
G
Ab
C
Male: Db
G
Ab
Female:
my kind of man. You're my kind of wom-an and you're

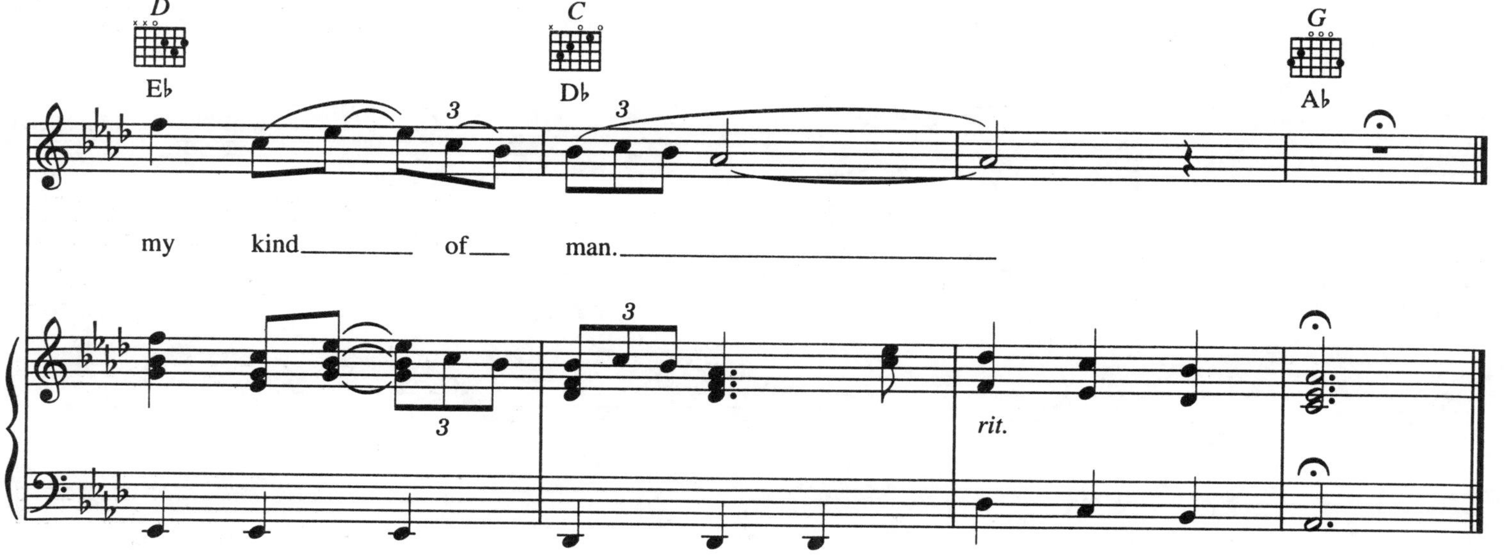
D
Eb
C
Db
G
Ab
my kind of man.
rit.

VALENTINE

Composed by
JIM BRICKMAN and JACK KUGELL

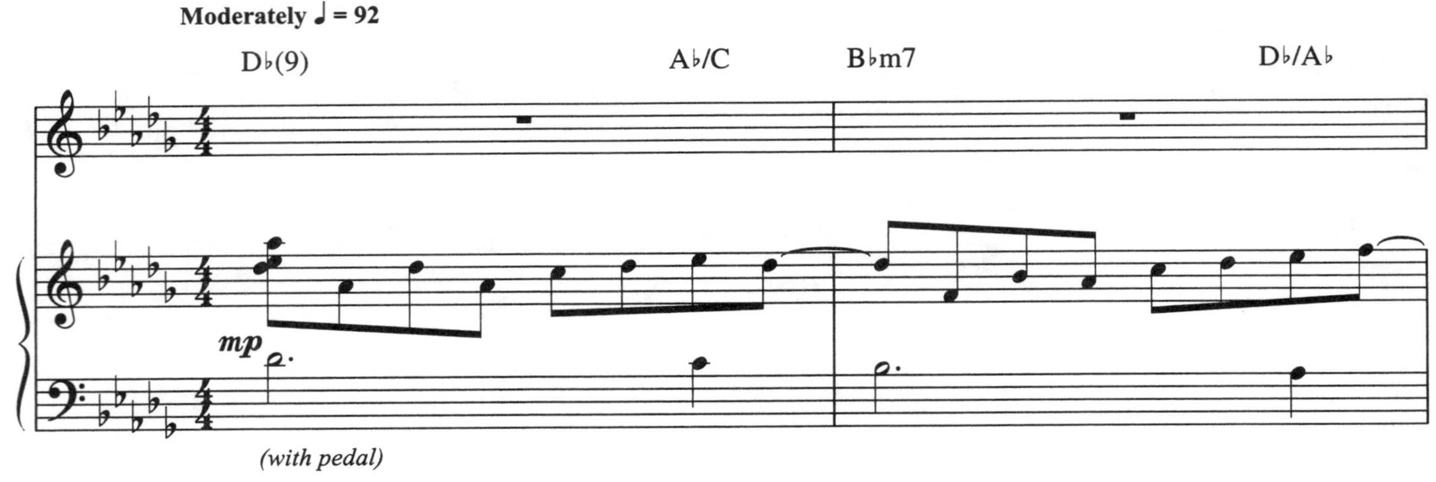

A♭sus A♭ D♭(9) B♭m7
would still hear you. If there were no tears, no way to feel
G♭(9) A♭7sus D♭(9)/F
inside, I'd still feel for you. And e - ven if the sun
G♭(9) A♭ Fm7 D♭(9)/F G♭(9) A♭
refused to shine, e - ven if ro - mance ran out of rhyme,
E♭m7 F7sus F7 B♭m D♭/A♭
you would still have my heart un - til the end of time.

Gm7(♭5)
D♭/A♭
G♭/A♭
You're all I need, my love, my Val - en - tine.
D♭(9)
A♭/C
B♭m7
D♭/A♭
G♭(9)
G♭/A♭
D♭(9)
B♭m7
G♭(9)
All of my life, I have been wait - ing for all
A♭sus
A♭
D♭(9)
B♭m7
you give to me. You've o - pened my eyes and shown me how

G♭(9)
A♭7sus
A♭
D♭(9)/F
to love un - self - ish - ly. I've dreamed of this a thou-
mf
G♭(9)
A♭
Fm7
D♭(9)/F
G♭(9)
A♭
- sand times be - fore, but in my dreams I could - n't love you more.
E♭m7
F7sus
F7
B♭m
D♭/A♭
I will give you my heart un - til the end of time.
Gm7(♭5)
D♭/A♭
G♭/A♭
You're all I need, my love, my Val - en - tine.

D♭(9)
B♭m7
G♭(9)
G♭/B♭
A♭/C
D♭(9)
B♭m7
G♭(9)
D♭/A♭
A♭
And
D♭(9)/F
G♭(9)
A♭
Fm7
D♭(9)/F
e - ven if the sun re - fused to shine, e - ven if ro - mance
G♭(9)
A♭
E♭m7
F7sus
F7
ran out of rhyme, you would still have my heart un - til

B♭m
D♭/A♭
Gm7(♭5)
D♭/A♭
the end of time.
'Cause all I need is you,
G♭/A♭
E♭m7
D♭/F
G♭
my Val - en - tine.
You're
mp
D♭/A♭
G♭/A♭
D♭(9)
A♭/C
all I need, my love, my Val - en - tine.
B♭m7
D♭/A♭
G♭(9)
G♭/A♭
D♭(9)
rit. e dim.
p

THE PRAYER

Italian Lyric by
ALBERTO TESTA and TONY RENIS

Words and Music by
CAROLE BAYER SAGER and DAVID FOSTER

F/A
B♭
Gm/C
and help us to be wise
in times when we don't
E♭/F
F
poco rit.
know.
Let this be our
poco rit.
Chorus:
Gm
Gm7/C
C7
A7sus
a tempo
prayer,
when we lose our
way.
a tempo
A7
Dm
B♭
Dm
Am
Lead us to a place,
guide us with your grace

B♭
F/C
C
B♭/F
F
to a place where we'll be safe.
Male:
mf
La lu - ce che tu
mf
Verse 2:
B♭
mf
C7sus
C7
F
I pray we'll find your light,
and hold it in our
dai,
nel cuo - re res - te - rá.
F/A
B♭
Csus
C
Gm/C
C
hearts
when stars go out each night,
A ri - cor - dar - ci che
l'e - ter - na ste - lla

E♭/F
F7
poco rit.
oh.
cresc.
poco rit.
sei.
Ne - lla mia pre -
cresc.
poco rit.
Chorus:
a tempo
Gm
Gm7/C
C7
A7sus
Let this be our prayer,
when sha - dows fill our
a tempo
ghie - ra
quan - ta fe - de c'é.
a tempo
f
A7
Dm
B♭
Dm
Am
mp
day.
guide us with your grace.
mp
Lead us to a place,
dim.
mp

B♭ F/C C7 B♭/F F
cresc.
Give us faith so we'll be safe. So - gna - mo un
Give us faith so we'll be safe. So - gna - mo un
cresc.
Bridge:
C/B♭ B♭ C/B♭ Fsus F C/B♭ B♭ C/B♭
mf
mon - do sen - za piú vio - len - za. Un mon - do di giu - sti - zia e di spe -
mon - do sen - za piú vio - len - za. Un mon - do di giu - sti - zia e di spe -
Fsus F B♭maj7 Fsus F Dm
ran - za. O - gnu - no dia la ma - no al suo vi - ci - no sim - bo - lo di
ran - za. O - gnu - no dia la ma - no al suo vi - ci - no sim - bo - lo di

D♭
B♭m
Fsus
F
cresc.
pa - ce, di tra - ter - ni - tá.
cresc.
pa - ce, di tra - ter - ni - tá.
La for - za che ci
cresc.
Verse 3:
E♭
Fsus
F
Fsus
F
B♭
f
We ask that life be kind,
and watch us from a -
f
dai
é il de - si - de - rio che.
f
B♭(9)/D
E♭
Fsus
F
bove.
We hope each soul will find
O - gnu - no tro - vi a - more
in - tor - no e den - tro

A♭/B♭
B♭
mf
an - oth - er soul to love. Let this be our
mf
sé. Let this be our
dim.
Chorus:
Cm
Cm7/F
F7
F7/E♭
D7sus
prayer, let this be our prayer, just like ev - 'ry
prayer, just like ev - 'ry child,
mf
D7
Gm
E♭
Gm
Dm
mp
child, need to find a place, guide us with your grace.
mp
need to find a place, guide us with your grace.
dim.
mp

E♭
B♭/F
F7
E♭/B♭
cresc.
B♭
B♭/A
Give us faith so we'll be safe.
cresc.
Give us faith so we'll be safe.
cresc.
Freely
Gm
mf
E♭
Gm
cresc.
f
Dm
E♭
mp
B♭/F
F7
molto rit.
E la fe - de che hai a - cce - so in noi. Sen - to che ci sal - ve -
mf
cresc.
f
mp
molto rit.
E la fe - de che hai a - cce - so in noi. Sen - to che ci sal - ve -
mf
cresc.
f
mp
molto rit.
G♭
A♭
B♭
rá.
rá.
p

YOU DON'T HAVE TO BE A STAR
(To Be in My Show)

Words and Music by
JAMES DEAN and JOHN GLOVER

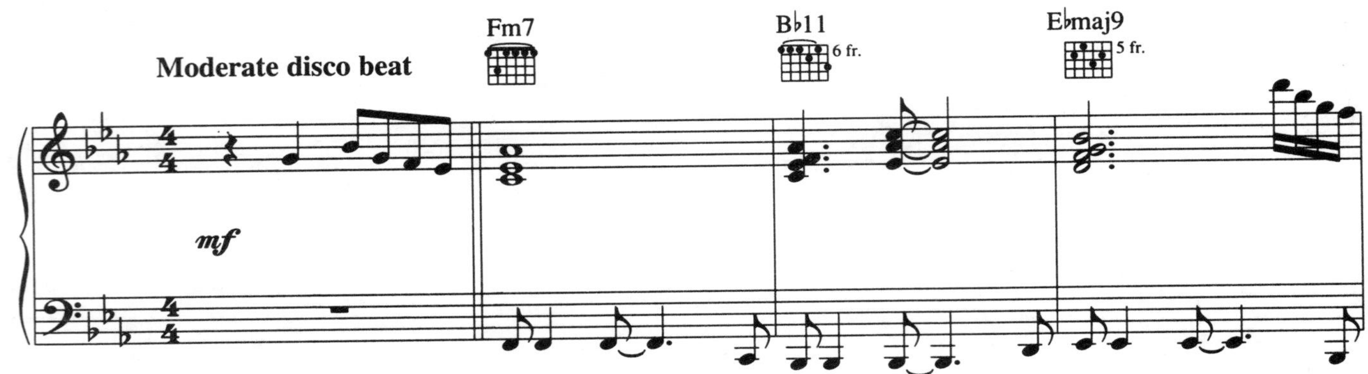

E♭maj7
E♭
A♭maj7
4 fr.
in; ___
hear, ___
though you're re - ject - ted and hurt, ___
so stop your run - ning a - round ___
to me, you're worth, ___
'cause now you've found ___
Fm7
E♭maj7
E♭
___ girl, what you have with - in. ___
___ what was cloud -y is clear. ___
Oh hon - ey boy, I don't need ___
Oh hon - ey, there'll be no cheer-
A♭
4 fr.
Fm7
E♭
G7
3 fr.
___ no su - per -star ___
ing from ___ the clouds; ___
'cause I'll ac - cept you as you are; ___
just two hearts ___ beat - ing out loud. ___

Cm7
3 fr.
Fm7
you won't be de - nied,
'cause I'm sat - is - fied
with the love
There'll be no pa - rade,
no T. V. or stage;
on - ly me
B♭11
6 fr.
Fm7
that you can in - spire.
'till your dy - ing day.
You don't have to be a star, ba - by,
f
B♭11
6 fr.
E♭
Cm
3 fr.
to be in my show;
oh, hon - ey, you don't have to be a

Fm7
Bb11
6 fr.
Eb
Ab/Eb
4 fr.
star, ba - by, to be in my show.
1.
2.
Eb
Eb
Fm7
Some - bo - dy no - bo - dy knows
mf
Bb11
6 fr.
Eb
Cm7
3 fr.
Fm7
Bb11
6 fr.
Ebmaj7
Ab/Eb
4 fr.
Ebmaj9
5 fr.

N.C.
A♭maj7
4 fr.
Fm7
Don't think your star has to shine ___ for me to find ___ out where you're com - ing from; _
E♭maj7
E♭
A♭maj7
4 fr.
oh, hon - ey, girl, what is a beau - ty queen ___ if it don't mean _
Fm7
E♭maj7
E♭
D.S. 𝄋 (lyric 1) and fade at chorus
that I'm num - ber one? ___ Oh, hon - ey, I don't need _

NOT TOO MUCH TO ASK

Words and Music by
DON SCHLITZ and
MARY-CHAPIN CARPENTER

F
F/A
B♭
F
Csus
just say I'll be the last.
F
C
B♭
F
B♭/D
C
It's too much to ex - pect,
but it's not too much to ask.
F
F/A
Bridge:
B♭
Both: Now I can on - ly
cresc.
dream
mf
of be - ing all you
F
F/A
B♭
need,
and I can on - ly try
Am
Gm/B♭
Csus
C
C/E
to be the rea - son why.
Female: You think a - bout to - day,
dim.

Verse:
F F/A B♭ F C/E
— (2nd time instr. solo. . .
mp-mf-mp
(1.) and for-get a-bout_ the past.
(2.) 'cause the past is just_ the past.
Dm F/C F/A Gm/B♭ To Coda Csus C C/E
Both: It's too much to_ ex-pect, but it's not too much
(Female only 3rd time)
F B♭/D C/E
to ask.
1. F B♭ C
cresc.
2. D.S. 𝄋 al Coda
F F/A
Both: Now I can on-ly
. . .end solo) cresc.
Coda A7sus A7 A7/C♯ Dm Dm/C G7/B G7
Male: but it does-n't hurt_ to ask. Both: It's too much to_
cresc.
dim.
Gm Csus C F B♭/D C F
_ ex-pect, Female: but it's not too much to ask.___
rit.

TONIGHT I CELEBRATE MY LOVE

Words and Music by
MICHAEL MASSER and GERRY GOFFIN

Eb
Cm7
Fm7
Ab/Bb
Ab
mf
night no one's gon - na find us, we'll leave the world be -
night our spir - its will be climb - ing to a sky lit up with
Gm7
Cm9
1.
Fm7
Ab/Bb
3
hind us, when I make love to you. 2. To -
dia - monds when I make
mp
2.
Abmaj7
Ab/Bb
Eb
Bb/Eb
love to you to - night.
Ab/Eb
To next strain
3.
Abmaj7
Ab/Bb
Bb
To - love to you. To -

Chorus:
Abmaj7
Gm7
Db/Eb
Eb7
night I cel - e - brate my love for you and the
f
mid - night sun is gon - na come shin - ing through. To -
Abmaj7
Gm7
Fm7
Cm7
night there'll be no dis - tance be - tween us. What I want
Abm(#7)
most to do is to get close to you to -
decresc.

Verse 3:
Tonight I celebrate my love for you,
And soon this old world will seem brand new.
Tonight we will both discover
How friends turn into lovers,
When I make love to you.
(To Chorus:)

YOUR LOVE

Words and Music by
JIM BRICKMAN, SEAN HOSEIN
and DANE DEVILLER

Am7
Dm7
F(9)
F/A
G/B
when I have you near beside me, here beside me.
Chorus:
C
Em7
F(9)
F/A
G/B
So you could give me wings to fly, and catch me if I fall.
C
Em7
F(9)
F/A
G/B
Or pull the stars down from the sky, so I can wish on them all.

Am7
Dm7
F(9)
Dm7/G
G
But I could-n't ask for more, 'cause your love is the great - est gift of all.

1.
C
C/E
F(9)
2.
C
Bridge:
Gm7
C
You could of - fer me the sun, the moon, and I would still be - lieve.
Fm7
E♭/G
Fm7/B♭
You gave me ev - 'ry - thing when you gave your heart to me.
E♭
E♭/G
A♭(9)
A♭/C
B♭/D

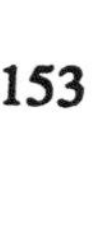

E♭ E♭/G A♭(9) A♭/C B♭/D

Cm7 Fm7 A♭(9) Fm7/B♭ B♭

But I could-n't ask__ for more,______ 'cause your love is the great - est gift__ of__ all.

Chorus:

E♭ Gm7 A♭(9) A♭/C B♭/D

So you could give__ me wings__ to fly,____ and catch me if____ I fall.__

E♭ Gm7 A♭(9) A♭/C B♭/D

__ Or pull the stars__ down from__ the sky,____ so I can wish on them all.__

Verse 2:
In your arms, I found a strength inside me.
And in your eyes, there's a light to guide me.
I would be lost without you.
And all that my heart could ever want has come true.
(To Chorus:)

A WHOLE NEW WORLD

Words by
TIM RICE

Music by
ALAN MENKEN

D
I can o - pen your eyes, take you won - der by
G/B
A/C♯
Em/G
F♯7
F♯7/A♯
Bm
Bm/A
won - der o - ver, side - ways and un - der, on a
G
D
Chorus:
A
mag - ic car - pet ride. A whole new world,
D
A
A7/C♯
A7
D(9)
D
a new fan - tas - tic point of view. No one to

G D/F♯ G D/F♯ Bm7 E7sus E7
tell us no, or where to go, or say we're on - ly dream -
G/A A D
Jasmine:
ing. A whole new world, a daz - zling
A A♯dim7 F♯7/A♯ Bm D7 G D/F♯
3
place I nev - er knew. But when I'm way up here, it's
G D/F♯ Bm7 E7sus E7 C A7sus A7
crys - tal clear, that now I'm in a whole new world with

Verse:
D
F
Jasmine:
you.
Un - be - liev - a - ble
Aladdin:
Now I'm in a whole new world with you.
Bb/D
C/E
sights, in - de - scrib - a - ble feel - ing.
Gm/Bb
A7sus
A7
Dm
Dm/C
Bb
Soar - ing, tum - bling, free - wheel - ing through an end - less dia - mond sky.

Chorus:
F
C
F
A whole new world, a hun - dred
Don't you dare close your eyes.
3
C
F
B♭
F/A
thou - sand things to see. I'm like a shoot - ing star, I've
Hold your breath, it gets bet - ter.
B♭
F/A
Dm
G7sus
G7
B♭/C
come so far I can't go back to where I used to
A whole new

C
F
C
C♯dim7
be. Ev - 'ry turn a sur - prise.
Ev - 'ry mo - ment red -
world
with new ho - ri - zons to pur - sue.
Dm
F7/C
B♭
F/A
B♭
F/A
let - ter. I'll chase them an - y - where. There's time to spare.
I'll chase them an - y - where. There's time to spare.
Dm
G7sus
G7
E♭
B♭/C
C7
Dm
Let me share this whole new world with you.
Let me share this whole new world with you.

F/C Bb(9) F/A Gm7(4)

A whole new world, that's where we'll

A whole new world, that's where we'll be.

F/A Bb(9) C7sus F

be. A won-d'rous place for you and me.

A thrill - ing chase for you and me.

rit.

Ped. *

SET THE NIGHT TO MUSIC

Words and Music by
DIANE WARREN

C/F
F
Look at all the stars to - night,
Let's find a rhy - thm all our own,
look at all that
melt in - to it
F/G
Gm7
3fr.
moon - light.
nice and slow.
Look at us, we're all
Love our - selves a - way
a - lone.
from here.
F
Bb
C
Oh, and it's just
Your heart beat - ing
like a dream,
next to mine,
like some ro - man - tic fan - ta - sy.
per - fect love in per - fect time.

F/G
Gm7
3fr.
F
C/F
F
C/F
Dar - ling, come and hold me close.
Watch the world just dis - ap - pear.
B♭
C
B♭(addC)/D
We could be mak - ing love, and with the slight -
The mo - ment is ours to take, and with the love
C/E
E
est touch we could
we make we could
A(addB)
A/B
E
set the night to mus - ic. We could

A(addB)
A/B
set the night to mus - ic.
We could
B(addC♯)/D♯
A(addB)/C♯
do what we want to do.
It would
C
To Coda
D
on - ly take me and you to
set the night to mus-
1.
E
C(addD)
ic.

2.
E
C/F
F
ic.
C/F
F
F/G
Gm7
3fr.
F
C/F
F
C/F
B♭
C/B♭
The mo - ment is ours to take,

B♭
C
B♭(addC)/D
and with the love we make,
and with the slight-
C/E
C
D.S. al Coda
est touch
we could
Coda
E
Repeat and fade
A
ic.
Set the night,
ic.)
A/B
E
set the night to mus-ic.
(Set the night to mus-

BY THE TIME THIS NIGHT IS OVER

Words and Music by
MICHAEL BOLTON, ANDY GOLDMARK
and DIANE WARREN

Cm7
3fr.
B♭
Cm7
3fr.
Si - lence takes o - ver, saying all we
Let's take a slow and ea - sy ride, lay back and let love
B♭
Cm7
3fr.
B♭(addC)/D
need to say. End - less pos - si - bil - i - ties in the
be the driv - er. There's mag - ic here with you and I, gon - na
F
F7
G♭maj9
moves we can make. Your kiss is giv - ing
take us all the way. Let's find some kind of
A♭
4fr.
G♭maj9
Cm7/F
8fr.
ev - ery in - di - ca - tion, and if this heart of mine is right,
deep con - ver - sa - tion, and ba - by, if it's right,
by the time this night is

F/B♭
B♭
F/B♭
B♭
F/G
Gm7
3fr.
o - ver, the stars are gon-na shine on two lov-ers in love.
o - ver.
Sax solo on D.S. 𝄋
F/G
Gm7
3fr.
E♭maj7
E♭6
E♭maj7
E♭6
And when the morn - ing comes, it's gon-na find us to-geth - er,
A♭maj7
4fr.
Cm7/F
8fr.
F/B♭
B♭
in a love that's just be - gun. By the time this night is o - ver,
F/B♭
B♭
F/G
Gm7
3fr.
F/G
Gm7
3fr.
two hearts are gon-na fly to the heav-ens a - bove. And we'll get

Ebmaj7
Eb6
To Coda
Cm7/F
8fr.
clos - er and clos - er and clos - er, by the time this night is
1. F/Bb
Bb
F/Bb
Bb
2. F/Bb
Bb
o - ver.
o - ver.
F/Bb
Bb
Dm7
A night like this may
Cm7
3fr.
Dm7
Cm7
3fr.
nev - er come a - gain.
And you won't want this night to end.

Em7
Cm7/F
8fr.
D.S. al Coda
Ba - by, we could have it all.
By the time this night is
Coda
Cm7/F
8fr.
Dm7/G
By the time this night is
G/C
C
G/C
C
G/A
3fr.
Am7
o - ver,
the stars are gon - na shine on two lov - ers in love.
G/A
3fr.
Am7
Fmaj7
F6
Fmaj7
F6
And when the morn - ing comes,
it's gon - na find us
to - geth - er,

B♭maj 7
Dm7/G
G/C
C
in a love that's just be - gun.
By the time this night is o - ver,
G/C
C
G/A
3fr.
Am7
G/A
3fr.
Am7
two hearts are gon - na fly to the heav - ens a - bove,
and we'll get
Repeat and fade (vocal ad lib)
Fmaj7
F6
Dm7
G/C
C
clos - er and clos - er and clos - er by the time this night is o - ver.
G/C
C
Fmaj7
F6
Fmaj7/G
Dm7/G
By the time this night is

WHEN SOMETHING IS WRONG WITH MY BABY

Words and Music by
ISAAC HAYES and DAVID PORTER

Em
Fm
A7
B♭7
She: We've been through so much to - geth - er.
Em
Fm
F7
G♭7
We stand as one, that's what makes it bet - ter.
C/G
D♭/A♭
Dm7
E♭m7
Both: When some-thing is wrong with my ba - by,
f
C/G
D♭/A♭
F
G♭
1.
C
D♭
F/G
G♭/A♭
G
A♭
2.
C
D♭
N.C.
some - thing is wrong with me.
me.

Additional Lyrics

2. *He:* Just what she means to me now,
Oh, you just wouldn't understand.
People can say that she's no good,
But ah, she's my woman and I know I'm her man.
She: And if he's got a problem,
Oh, I know I got to help him solve 'em.
Both: When something is wrong with my baby,
Something is wrong with me.